Letterland

Grammar

Prefixes and suffixes

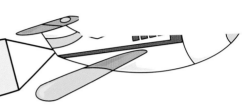

This book belongs to:

Giving a child an analogy they can relate to has always been the key to Letterland's success. *Letterland Grammar* describes stories as towns; within those towns there are streets, or sentences. The words we see are the buildings, and just as buildings are modified, extended or developed, so words change with the addition of prefixes, suffixes and tenses. Punctuation is represented by road signs.

In *Letterland Grammar*, as your child reads, they are encouraged to think of their finger on the page as a car travelling along a street looking out for 'reading' signs along the way. Use the 'Little car' finger puppet to bring this idea to life!

Stop, look, listen!
Read through these sections with your child. It's important that the concept is introduced clearly first.

Get set
These are examples to work through together slowly. Give your child support and encouragement as they complete the activities.

Go!
Encourage your child to have a go at these activities on their own.

Contents of Activity Book 3

Words are like buildings that can be changed, developed and extended.
Prefixes and suffixes are like the porches or extensions we can add to houses.
The structure of the house remains the same, but the function or use is extended. In this book, children learn to use different types of suffixes and are also introduced to compound nouns.

Stop, look, listen!

There are lots of different types of buildings in towns - houses, flats, offices, shops, cafés. The different buildings in a street can be a bit like the different types of words in a sentence.

Nouns

These are the words that *name things* such as people, places or objects. Let's think of the houses on a street as the **nouns**.

Verbs

A verb is a word that *describes* actions and activities. Let's think of work places, such as offices or factories as the **verbs**.

Suffixes

A **suffix** is a letter or letters added to the end of a **noun** or **verb** *to make a new word*. Let's think of a **suffix** as an extension. Extensions can change the way we use a building.

apple

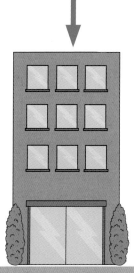

eat

apples

Nouns are the words that name things such as people, places or objects. Draw a line to match the **noun** with its picture.

house

dog

fish

tree

key

The nouns above are all **singular nouns** - there is *only one* of each thing. Sometimes we want to talk about *more than one* of something. When we do we have to use a **plural noun**.

Use the stickers to show what letter or letters have been added to make each of these **plural nouns**.

STICKER TIME!

one **cat**   lots of **cats**

one **bus**   lots of **buses**

one **baby**   lots of **babies**

The letter or letters that we add to the end of a word to make a new word are called a **suffix**. Think of a **suffix** like an extension added to the side of a house.

5

Most **singular nouns** are turned into a **plural noun** by adding the suffix **-s**.

Add the **suffix -s** to change these **singular nouns** into **plural nouns**.

I ate an apple. She ate two _____ .

She chose one book. He chose three _____ .

If the **singular noun** ends in any of the letters in the box below, then we have to add the **suffix -es** to make it a **plural noun**. (This **-es** plural often sounds like **-is**).

-s	-ss	-x	-z	-ch	-sh

Add the **suffix -es** to change these **singular nouns** into **plural nouns**.

Mum waited ages for the bus, then two _____

came at the same time.

I could only carry one box, but my friend could carry two _____ .

If the **singular noun ends in a vowel** (**a**, **e**, **i**, **o**, **u**) followed by a '**y**' then just add '**s**' to make the **plural noun**.

If the **singular noun ends in a consonant followed by a 'y'**, change the '**y**' to an '**i**' and add **-es** to make the **plural noun**.

boy   →   boys   baby   →   babies

Change the '**y**' to an '**i**' and add the **suffix -es** to change these **singular nouns** into **plural nouns**.

We thought our dog would have one puppy, but she

ended up with three _____ .

I got a book out at my local library but I can return it to any of the

_____ in the area.

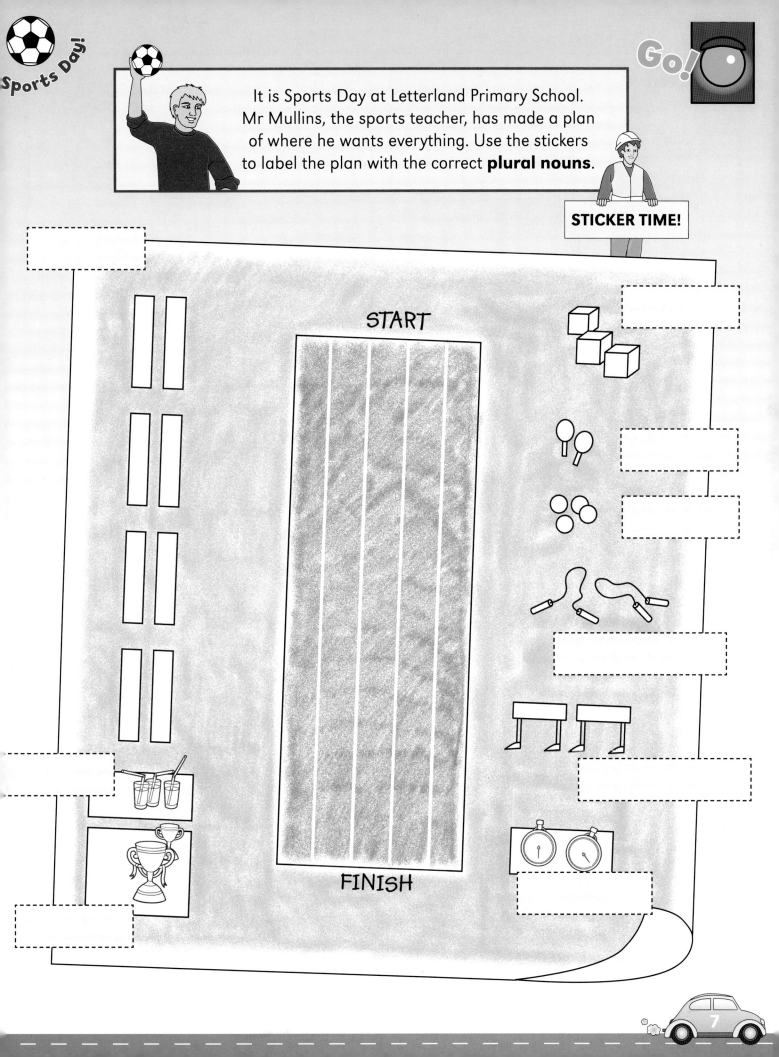

It is Sports Day at Letterland Primary School. Mr Mullins, the sports teacher, has made a plan of where he wants everything. Use the stickers to label the plan with the correct **plural nouns**.

STICKER TIME!

START

FINISH

Stop, look, listen!

A **verb** is a word that *describes actions and activities.*

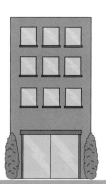

Think of verbs like offices or factories where there is a lot of activity.

I can jump.   Do you want to play?

Get set...

Circle the **verbs** in these sentences.

The rabbit can eat a lot of carrots.

Can you climb that tree?

Change these words into new words by adding the **suffix -ing**.
The first one has been done for you.

Root word (verb)	+ suffix	New word
jump		jumping
work	+ ing	
talk		

Change these words into new words by adding the **suffix -ed**.

Root word (verb)	+ suffix	New word
stay		
pull	+ ed	
open		

The children are talking about their Sports Day. Use the stickers to add the correct **suffix** to the **verbs**. Be careful, some of the **verbs** *may not need a* **suffix** *at all.*

STICKER TIME!

Last year, I kick ___ the ball into the trees by mistake!

I love pull ___ in the tug-of-war.

I'll be cheer ___ for you.

My mum is help ___ with the drinks.

I have to wait a long time for my race.

We play ___ chase ___ at lunchtime so I'm already tired.

My teacher said we should wait here.

Are you better at throw ___ or catch ___?

Ssh, Miss says we shouldn't be talk ___.

9

When we add letters to the beginning of a word to make a new one, it is called a **prefix**. Think of a **prefix** like a porch that we add to the front of a house or building.

The **prefix un-** is really powerful.
Although it doesn't change the spelling of the root word it *completely changes its meaning,* like this:

Can you please tie my shoelace?

Can you please untie my shoelace?

Get set...

Add the **prefix un-** to these root words to give them the *opposite meaning.*

kind

lucky   load

Underline the **root word**. Circle the **prefix**.

unwise   undo   unpack   unroll   unafraid

Rewrite this sentence, adding the **prefix un-** to the word in **bold**. See how it changes the meaning of the sentence.

She was **afraid** of the monster.

Before the races begin, the headteacher of Letterland Primary School welcomes everybody and gives out some messages. Unfortunately, the microphone isn't working very well and it is hard for the parents to hear some of the words. Circle the words that make sense in the speech below.

Good afternoon everybody.

I hope you've had a pleasant / an unpleasant lunch and that you're looking forward to this afternoon's events. Just a few notices before we get started.

We don't want anybody to be safe / unsafe so please keep behind the rope, away from the running track at all times.

There are drinks available / unavailable; please help yourself. If anyone feels well / unwell, please go to our first aid area.

We don't like our school grounds to be tidy / untidy so please put any rubbish in the bin.

It would be helpful / unhelpful if you could collect your child from their teacher after the prizes have been given. Please remember to bring a clean / an unclean sports kit back to school on Monday.

We hope that you and all of the children will go home feeling happy / unhappy having had a forgettable / an unforgettable afternoon of fun and games.

Enjoy the afternoon.

Stop, look, listen!

The **suffix -er** can be used to turn a **verb** into a **noun**.

climb → add the **suffix -er** → climb**er**

Get set...

Fill in the missing words below.

Verb (what a person is doing)	+ suffix	Noun (the person who does the verb)
teach		
clean		
		owner
	+ er	buyer
sing		
		helper

Sometimes a **noun suffix** won't work unless *other letters change*.

For example, if we add the **suffix -er** to a word that ends in a single vowel and a single consonant, we must *double the consonant and then add the **suffix***.

run → runner

single vowel
single consonant

double the
consonant
then add **-er**

Add the **suffix -er** to these **verbs** to make a **noun**. Remember to *double the consonant before adding the **suffix***.

rob _____

swim _____

plan _____

rub _____

12

Turning verbs into nouns (suffix -ness)

An **adjective** is a word that makes a **noun** *more specific*.

Adjectives can be turned into **nouns** by adding the **suffix -ness**. As well as naming things such as people, places or objects, a **noun** can also name a feeling or the way something is.

a red house

The **redness** on her skin may be sunburn.

Add the **suffix '-ness'** to the **adjectives** to make these sentences correct.

There was _____ in her voice. (**sad**)

His _____ stopped him from putting up his hand. (**shy**)

The _____ of the sun blinded them for a moment when they came out of the _____ of the cave. (**bright / dark**)

There was a lot of _____ at school last term. (**sick**)

Stop, look, listen!

Most **nouns** are words in their own right, a bit like detached houses. However, there are some **nouns** that are *created from two words* that work well as one word. Think of this as creating a large house by knocking two smaller houses together.

bed   room   →   bedroom

Get set...

Put a circle around the **nouns**.

rain	swim	coat	jump	tooth	climb
room	brush	foot	ball	bath	sing

Look at the **nouns** you have circled. Which **compound nouns** can you make with them?
One has been done for you.

1. [rain] + [coat] = *raincoat*

2. [ ] + [ ] =

3. [ ] + [ ] =

4. [ ] + [ ] =

These pictures are of **compound nouns**. Find two words on the right that go together to make the **compound noun**, then write the **compound noun**.

shell   board

man   sea

skate   snow

Stop, look, listen!

Sometimes the two words that work together to create a **compound noun** are kept separate, with a space between them.

washing   machine   →   washing machine

Get set...

Pair up the words below to make **compound nouns** that are *two words*.

Write your new **compound nouns** here. Remember to keep the space.

mobile	pan
post	phone
frying	car
bus	park
swimming	stop
car	box
racing	pool

1. mobile phone
2.
3.
4.
5.
6.
7.

Some types of **compound nouns** are like joining two houses together with a corridor or hyphen to connect them.

t - shirt

15

STICKER TIME!

Find the **compound nouns** in these photographs of Letterland Primary School's Sports Day. Use the stickers to label them.

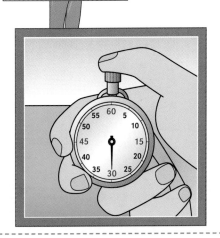

water

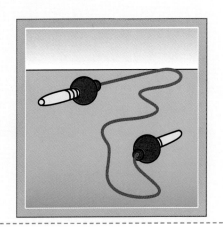

Creating adjectives (suffixes -ful and -less)

Often we make little additions to our houses. We add window boxes, solar panels, festive lights or even flags. These additions may be temporary but they add to the building. They give us extra information or can even change the way we use a building.

In a similar way, adding the **suffix -ful** can change the meaning of some words and *turn them into* **adjectives**.

care + ful → careful

Get set...

Change these words to **adjectives** by adding the **suffix -ful**.

Root word	+ suffix	New word (adjective)
hope		
peace	**+ ful**	
forget		

Choose one of the **adjectives** you have made and write a sentence using it.

---

care + less = careless

careful   careless

What is the new **suffix**?

What do you notice about the *meaning* of the two **adjectives**?

Notice how adding the **suffix -ful** *adds the meaning 'full of'*, while **-less** indicates *something missing or taken away*.

Root word	+ suffix	New word (adjective)
hope		
help	**+ less**	
rest		

Choose one of the **adjectives** you have made and write a sentence using it.

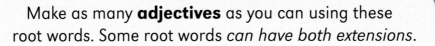
Make as many **adjectives** as you can using these root words. Some root words *can have both extensions*.

cheer

power

use

success

help

colour

wish

price

point

pain

+ ful

+ less

Remember, when you enlarge a building, sometimes you need to alter something about the building before you add the extra part - for example, by knocking down a wall or adding an extra pillar for strength.

In the same way, sometimes letters in the root word need to change before you add **-er** or **-est**. These **two suffixes** create **adjectives** that make comparisons between things.

The **suffix -er** compares *two things*.
The **suffix -est** compares *more than two things*.

The cat is small.

The rabbit is smaller.

The mouse is smallest.

The plain cake is nice.

The fruit cake is nicer.

The chocolate cake is nicest.

Here are some rules to help you remember what to do.

If an **adjective** ends in e, knock it off before you add the **suffix**.

rude

ruder

rudest

If an **adjective** ends in a single consonant, it needs extra strength to support the suffixes, so add the same consonant again.

hot

hotter

hottest

If an **adjective** ends in y, it needs a different letter put in its place so change the 'y' to 'i'.

pretty

prettier

prettiest

Use the rules from page 19 to correctly complete these reports of Letterland Primary School's Sports Day.

fast

In the boys' running race

Jack was _____ ,

Noah was _____

and Ethan was

the _____ .

long

Ben's jump was _____ ,

Jackson's jump was

_____ and

Mia's jump was

the _____ .

loud

The cheers from the teachers were _____ , the

cheers from the parents were _____ , but the

cheers from the children were the _____ .

wobbly

It was fun to watch people on the balance beam.

Ryan was _____ ,

Olivia was _____

and Nathan was

the _____ .

big

Alex's throw was _____ ,

Ella's throw was _____

and Jacob's throw was

the _____ .

Stop, look, listen!

Let's learn about **adverbs** - the words that *describe how an action is done*.

The black dog barked loudly.

This sentence tells us that the dog (**noun**) was barking (**verb**) and the **adverb** tells us how it was barking - loudly!

Get set...

Underline the **verb** in these sentences - *the action or activity word* - and circle the **adverb** - the word that tells you *how that action is being done*.

The children ate the cake (quickly.)

Bravely, Jack climbed up the ladder.

Daniel was playing with his friends nicely.

Which **suffix** do you notice at the end of each of the **adverbs**?

Sometimes spellings change when you use the **suffix -ly** to make an **adverb**.

If a word ends in '**y**', change the '**y**' to '**i**' and add **-ly**.	If a word ends in '**le**', drop off the '**e**' and add **-y**.	If a word ends in '**ic**', add **-ally**.
happy	**terrible**	**basic**
becomes	becomes	becomes
happily	**terribly**	**basically**

The parents and children walk home from Sports Day, talking about the afternoon's events. Complete the sentences using words with the **suffix -ly**. Check how to spell the words correctly by using the rules on page 21.

The children in your class sat really _____ all afternoon. (**quiet**)

Did you see how _____ I walked on the balance beam? (**careful**)

You were cheering really _____ . (**loud**)

Our teacher said that we'd all behaved _____ . (**sensible**)

When you fell over, you got up _____ and carried on the race. I was proud of you. (**brave**)

This was _____ the best Sports Day ever! (**definite**)

Can you use what you've learnt in this activity book in your own writing?
Have a go at these challenges and see how well you do.

Challenge 1
A local reporter has written about Letterland Primary School's Sports Day in the local newspaper. Read the report and underline any suffixes you've learnt about in this activity book. This is a great chance to see how **suffixes** can be used to make words fit properly into a sentence.

Super Sports Day!

The sun was shining as the children of Letterland Primary School waited excitedly to take part in their sports day. Some children were runners; other children took part in jumping, throwing or balancing challenges. Every child had to run in the relay race. They were all fast, but the blue team was the fastest. Everyone cheered loudly and supported each other brilliantly.

How well did you do?
Give yourself one point for each **suffix** you underlined.
If you got more than 10, you're a suffix superstar!

Points scored:

'I can do' reward chart

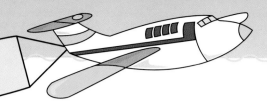

Prefixes and suffixes

Give yourself a smiley face sticker for each section of this book you complete.
Look out for the prefixes and suffixes you've learnt about in this book
when you read. Use them when you write too.

My name is:

I can...

○ understand which singular nouns need the suffix -s and which need the suffix -es to make them plural.

○ say what a root word and a verb is.

○ understand that some suffixes can be added to verbs without changing the root word.

○ understand that the prefix un- changes the meaning of a word to a negative.

○ understand how the suffixes -er and -ness can be used to form nouns.

○ understand that two separate words can be combined to form a compound noun, with or without spaces between the two words.

○ say what an adjective is.

○ recognise where and how the spelling of some root words change when adding the suffixes -ful and -less.

○ say what an adverb is.

○ recognise where and how the spelling of some root words change when adding the suffix -ly.